KIDS CAN'T STOP READING THE *CHOOSE YOUR OWN ADVENTURE*® STORIES!

"I like *Choose Your Own Adventure*® books because they're full of surprises. I can't wait to read more."
—Cary Romanos, age 12

"Makes you think thoroughly before making a decision."
—Hassan Stevenson, age 11

"I have read five different stories in one night and that's a record for me. The different endings are fun."
—Timmy Sullivan, age 9

"It's great fun! I like the idea of making my own decisions."
—Anthony Ziccardi, age 11

AND TEACHERS LIKE THIS SERIES, TOO!

"We have read and reread,
wo ... for others,
... , the
C ... books."

CH ... NTURE®—
AND M ... RE FUN!

Bantam Books in the Choose Your Own Adventure® Series
Ask your bookseller for the books you have missed

CHOOSE YOUR OWN ADVENTURE® • 8

DEADWOOD CITY

BY EDWARD PACKARD

ILLUSTRATED BY PAUL GRANGER

BANTAM BOOKS
TORONTO · NEW YORK · LONDON · SYDNEY

RL 5, IL Age 10 and up

DEADWOOD CITY

A Bantam Book / published by arrangement with
Harper & Row, Publishers, Inc.

PRINTING HISTORY
Lippincott edition published January 1978
2nd printing . . . . June 1979
Bantam edition / November 1980
2nd printing . . . . . . March 1981 4th printing . . . December 1981
3rd printing . . . . July 1981 5th printing . . . . April 1982
6th printing . . . . . . August 1982

Original Conception of Edward Packard

Illustrated by Paul Granger

CHOOSE YOUR OWN ADVENTURE® is a
trademark of Bantam Books, Inc.

ISBN 0-553-23230-4

Published simultaneously in the United States and Canada

Bantam Books are published by Bantam Books, Inc. Its trademark, consisting of the words "Bantam Books" and the portrayal of a rooster, is Registered in U.S. Patent and Trademark Office and in other countries. Marca Registrada. Bantam Books, Inc., 666 Fifth Avenue, New York, New York 10103.

PRINTED IN THE UNITED STATES OF AMERICA

O 15 14 13 12 11 10 9 8 7

To Caroline, Andrea, and Wells

DEADWOOD CITY

WARNING!!!!

Do not read this book straight through from beginning to end! These pages contain many different adventures you can have in the Old West. From time to time as you read along, you will be asked to make a choice. Your choice may lead to success or disaster!

The adventures you take are a result of your choice. *You* are responsible because *you* choose! After you make your choice follow the instructions to see what happens to you next.

Remember—you cannot go back! Think carefully before you make a move! One mistake can be your last . . . or it *may* lead you to fame and fortune!

Imagine yourself . . .
on horseback,
riding along a desert trail,
humming a tune.

In the distance you can see the snowcapped peaks of the Rocky Mountains.

You have been working as a cowhand in the Old West. But your last job was boring, so about a week ago you packed up and headed on to Deadwood City. Now you are finally approaching your destination.

It is late afternoon. It is a warm, dry day, and as you ride into town a fresh breeze blows the dust up into swirling clouds.

The streets are nearly deserted, and the few people you see seem nervous and tense. You wonder what to do. You might go over to the saloon and see what's happening there. You know that in a Western town there is no better place to pick up the news than the saloon. But maybe you should go to the hotel. The clerk at the front desk can probably tell you what's doing in Deadwood City. Besides, you need a place to stay for the night. Then again, you might go to the sheriff's office. If there is trouble in Deadwood City, the sheriff is likely to know about it.

If you decide to go to the saloon, turn to page 5.

If you decide to go to the hotel, turn to page 6.

If you decide to go to the sheriff's office, turn to page 7.

You walk over to the saloon. There are about ten people sitting at the bar. A bald man is at a piano, chewing on a cigar and banging out an old tune. Everyone looks around nervously when you walk in. You sit down at a table and order something to drink. Some cardplayers nearby ask you if you'd like to be dealt in on a game of poker. You say, "Sure, why not?" It seems like a good chance to meet some people.

One guy says, "You know what the stakes in this game are? The loser has to go out and take care of Kurt Malloy."

"Who's Kurt Malloy?" you ask.

"King of the outlaws, that's who he is. He's coming to town, and it's up to one of us to stop him!"

If you decide to stay and play cards, turn to page 8.

If you decide to walk out of the saloon, turn to page 10.

You walk over to the hotel. The lobby is dark and dingy. The walls are hung with old wagon wheels and badly painted pictures of mountains. A few moth-eaten rugs lie on the floor.

"Can I get a room for the night?" you ask the desk clerk.

He glances around the lobby before speaking to you. "Sure," he replies. "You'll have a good view of the action when Kurt Malloy comes into town."

"Who's Kurt Malloy?"

"If you don't know who Kurt Malloy is, you're in bigger trouble than everyone else, and that's plenty of trouble. He's the meanest man in the West. He rides with a gang of desperadoes, and the word is he's going to take over this town. Even the sheriff is scared to death."

The situation doesn't look too good. This third-rate hotel is just the kind of place Kurt Malloy might take over before he takes over the rest of the town. On the other hand, you need a place to stay and something to eat.

If you decide to check into the hotel, turn to page 11.

If you decide to go outside and maybe find someplace else to stay, turn to page 12.

You walk down the dusty street until you come to a shack with a sign over it saying SHERIFF'S OFFICE. You go inside and are greeted by a tall, thin-faced man wearing a tin star on his shirt. You introduce yourself to him, and he invites you to have a seat.

"Have you heard what's going on?" he asks. "Kurt Malloy is coming into town. When he takes over a town, it might just as well have been burned down. In fact, if you ask me, that would be preferable. All I can say is, you'd better watch your step."

You think maybe this town isn't such a great place to be, but you're just about broke, and you'd better stay around long enough to earn some money.

"Do you have any idea where I might get a job?" you ask.

"No, I don't," the sheriff replies, "but you might talk to Mrs. Megan. She lives right across the street, and she always seems to know everything that's going on around here."

If you decide to pay a call on Mrs. Megan, turn to page 14.

If you decide you'll look around town instead, turn to page 15.

You play a few hands of poker. Your luck is good and you win five silver dollars. Then someone shouts that Malloy and his gang are riding into town.

"Okay," says the dealer. "The next hand is to see who goes out to meet Kurt Malloy."

He deals out five cards to each player. You pick up your hand and look at the cards. You have the eight of clubs and the three, the five, the eight, and the jack of hearts. The rules allow you to throw down three cards and pick up three new ones.

If you keep the eights, you will at least have one pair, and you might pick up another eight, making three of a kind; but if you could get another heart in exchange for the eight of clubs you would have a flush, and that would be almost sure to beat any other hand.

If you throw down everything but the pair of eights, turn to page 16.

If you throw down only the eight of clubs and try for a flush, turn to page 17.

As you pass the bar on your way out of the saloon, you overhear a couple of cowhands talking.

"They've discovered a lot of gold in California," one of them says, "and there could be some around here. I've heard there's plenty up in Bald Mountain. That might be the place to go."

You walk up and get into the conversation. Before the evening is over, the two cowhands, Lefty and Jake, have asked you to come prospecting with them. The idea sounds good, so the next morning you buy some gear from the local store and the three of you head toward Bald Mountain.

As you leave town, you see some men on horseback riding down the main street looking as if they owned it. You know it must be Kurt Malloy and his gang.

You chose the right time to get out, but as you ride along, you begin to worry about Lefty and Jake. After all, you hardly know them. Maybe you'd do better on your own.

If you decide to stick with your new companions, turn to page 18.

If you decide to leave them and ride on by yourself, turn to page 19.

You check into the hotel and walk up the dimly lit stairs and through a deserted hallway to your room. It is small and shabby. Through the window you can see the main street and the mountains in the distance.

Just as you are lying down to take a little rest after your hard day's ride, you hear a commotion in the room next door. It sounds as if people are throwing furniture all over the place. After a while the fighting stops, but now you can hear a couple of drunks singing in another room. They sound worse than a pack of coyotes. You are having a hard time getting any rest.

If you get up and go out for a walk,
turn to page 20.

If you ignore the noise and stay in your room, turn to page 21.

Outside the setting sun is so bright that you have to squint to see straight. When your eyes have adjusted to the light, you find yourself staring at the meanest-looking man you have ever seen. You know it must be Kurt Malloy. The three men riding up behind him do not look any nicer.

Ignoring the other people on the street, Malloy rides straight toward you. He brings his horse to a stop and looks down at you contemptuously. "I'm not sure I want you in this town, kid," he says.

If you decide to tell Malloy that you don't want him in this town either, turn to page 22.

If you decide to keep cool and avoid trouble, turn to page 24.

13

You knock on Mrs. Megan's door. In a moment it opens, and a little old woman with sparkling blue eyes and a warm smile greets you. When you tell her the sheriff suggested you pay her a call and that you are looking for work, she invites you to join her for a cup of tea.

"You could get a job as a ranch hand, or even riding shotgun, if you like that sort of work," Mrs. Megan says. "Just look at the notices posted down at Tyler's general store. But would you consider starting a newspaper? I've been planning to do it myself. I even had a printing press sent all the way from Philadelphia, but now my health isn't what it used to be, and I'm just not up to it. If you're interested, I'll help you set up."

If you decide to check out the notices at the general store, turn to page 15.

If you decide to go into the newspaper business, turn to page 40.

You stroll over to Tyler's general store. There are several notices posted on the wall, and two of them advertise job openings. One says:

Sounds good. You could make some money, see the countryside, and meet lots of people. But that job could also be a one-way ticket to the grave.

The other notice says:

If you decide to apply for the job riding shotgun, turn to page 28.

If you decide to head over to the Red Creek Ranch, turn to page 30.

The cards you draw are useless, but at least you still have the pair of eights. The poor fellow across from you has only a pair of fours. He reluctantly walks outside to wait for Kurt Malloy.

Others join the game, and soon everyone is playing for higher and higher stakes. You could lose your horse, your saddle, and your shirt. But you've done well so far, and this could be your chance to make a small fortune.

If you decide to quit and go over to the hotel, turn to page 11.

If you decide to gamble for the big stakes, turn to page 32.

If you decide to pocket your money and go play at another table where the stakes are lower, turn to page 33.

You draw the six of spades—which leaves you with a worthless hand. "Tough, chum," the guy next to you says. "You lost, and you'll have to go out and wait for Kurt Malloy."

You know there is no choice. Malloy and his gang are about to ride into town, and you have been appointed official greeter. You slowly walk through the swinging doors.

Turn to page 12.

You'll go along with Jake and Lefty—for a while, anyway. At least there is lots of beautiful scenery to look at. That night you make camp near a fast-flowing stream. Nearby is a waterfall, and below it a sparkling pool where you can take a little swim.

You enjoy Jake's company, but there is something about Lefty you do not like. He keeps bragging about what a great rider he is and what a great hunter he is. You wonder why he feels the need to carry on like that. Still, you don't give it too much thought.

Every evening, after a hard day's prospecting for gold, the three of you sit around the campfire and talk about how rich you will become. But day after day goes by, and you don't find any gold. You wonder whether it is worthwhile to look further.

If you decide to stick it out a little longer, turn to page 34.

If you decide to take off and seek your fortune elsewhere, turn to page 36.

You ride on and on. Suddenly, out of nowhere, an Indian on horseback appears, holding his right hand up in a gesture of peace.

He speaks a little English, and he seems friendly enough. After a while you understand that he is from a nearby Navaho village. His people have sent him to look for someone to teach them English, and he tells you that you will be rewarded if you help them.

If you decide to go with the Indian to his village, turn to page 37.

If you decide not to go with him, turn to page 38.

As you walk out of the hotel you notice a poster tacked up next to the door.

You realize that quite a few ranch owners will be attending. One of them might be able to use another cowhand, and you need a job.

As you stand there, a tall, slim man with a weather-beaten face comes up.

"Looking for a job, friend?" he asks.

"I'm thinking about it," you reply.

"Well, let me introduce myself," the stranger says. "I'm Jim Putney of the Sunrise Ranch—it's just a couple of miles north of here. We're going to be raising a lot of sheep on our spread, and if you'll ride up tomorrow noontime, we'll probably have a job for you."

If you decide to go to the Eagle Ranch and look for work as a cowhand, turn to page 39.

If you decide to head out to the Sunrise Ranch instead, turn to page 66.

Soon the noise dies down. Now the town seems as quiet as a graveyard, and you know why they call it Deadwood City.

You've heard there's a big ranch nearby called the T-Bar where you might be able to get work, so the next morning you saddle up early and ride on out there. The buildings and fences are run down and in need of repair, but the owner seems to be friendly, and he offers you a job as a ranch hand.

While you're talking with him, a deputy sheriff rides up to the corral. He says he needs people who are good shots to help capture Kurt Malloy. You will have a chance to share in the reward if you join the posse. On the other hand, it could be dangerous. And the owner of the T-Bar says he'll give you the job only if you start right away.

If you decide to take the job at the ranch,
turn to page 69.

If you decide to join the posse,
turn to page 70.

You walk right up and say, "You're Kurt Malloy, aren't you?"

Malloy replies, "And who do you think you are?"

"I hear you're planning to take over this town," you say.

"You've got the picture," Malloy answers.

"Well, Malloy," you say, "I'm here to tell you that this town doesn't want you."

He goes for his gun, but you are ready for him, and you draw, too.

Turn to page 42.

You don't want to risk a fight right now, so you start walking away.

Malloy says, "Come back here, pal, if you aren't looking for trouble."

If you decide to obey Malloy's order, turn to page 44.

If you decide to just keep walking, turn to page 45.

"Well, why not?" you ask yourself. That seems to be where the action and the money are.

So you join Malloy and his friends.

Malloy gives a little talk: "I've got this town where I want it, but there's only one problem. That sheriff is a thorn in my side. He's a miserable cur, but he could cause trouble. Now, I don't believe in breaking the law. I just believe in changing it a little. I'm going to have a drink at the saloon. Meet me here in half an hour, and we'll go over and make *me* the sheriff of this town."

If you are having second thoughts about being in the gang and decide to pull out quietly while Malloy is in the saloon, turn to page 41.

If you decide to help Malloy take over the sheriff's office, turn to page 46.

Your editorial states that for years cattle ranchers have been able to let their stock graze freely. Why, you ask your readers, should they now have their grazing land ruined by sheep ranchers?

Some of the cattlemen drop into your office and congratulate you on doing a good job. Other readers complain that you are for giving cattle ranchers all the public land.

After a while, you begin to have second thoughts. The railroads are bringing more and more people to the West. Many farmers and sheep ranchers are settling in the area. Maybe it's time the cattlemen learned to respect the rights of others. You just don't know which side is right, but you're afraid that if your doubts are reflected in the *Dispatch*, people will think you don't know your own mind and will stop reading your newspaper.

If you feel you must consider the arguments for both sides, turn to page 50.

If you feel that you should just stick to the policy you have followed up to now, turn to page 51.

You spend a few days calling on sheep ranchers in the area. They argue that the cattlemen are breaking the law by fencing off water holes and trying to drive sheep ranchers off public land.

You decide the sheep ranchers have just cause for complaint, and in the following Friday's edition of the *Dispatch* you print an editorial saying so.

Many people comment favorably on your editorial, but a couple of mornings later, several tough-looking men stop you in the street. They are led by Jack Garvey, a burly, red-bearded cattle rancher.

"We like your newspaper a lot," Garvey says. "It would be a shame if you weren't around to run it anymore."

You know that you can't run a newspaper by letting other people tell you what to write. On the other hand, you've heard about a lot of dead heroes in the West, and you don't want to be one of them.

If you continue to publish your views on the rights of sheep ranchers, turn to page 47.

If you decide to write about other things for a while, turn to page 49.

The stagecoach company hires you to ride shotgun. Your job will be to ride along and defend the coach against anyone who attacks it. The dispatcher tells you that you can choose one of two trips for your first assignment. You can go on the stagecoach with a gold shipment bound for San Francisco. This could be a dangerous trip,

but you will get extra pay. Or you can ride with the mail shipment to Santa Fe, which will be safer but will pay less.

If you decide to ride with the gold shipment, turn to page 52.

If you decide to ride with the mail shipment, turn to page 53.

You saddle up and ride to the Red Creek Ranch. You are lucky—Mr. Griswold, the owner, offers you a good job there. Charley Jackson, who is one of the other cowhands, shows you around and introduces you to everybody. The ranch seems like a good place to work, but the next evening, Charley takes you aside.

"Watch out for Larson," Charley warns you. "He's one of the meanest varmints around, and for some reason he doesn't seem to like you."

A couple of days later, Larson comes up to you while you're pitching hay. "Look, kid," he says, "there isn't room enough here for me and you both, and that means there isn't room enough for you. You know what I mean?"

If you decide to ignore Larson's threat, turn to page 54.

If you decide to discuss the problem with Mr. Griswold, turn to page 55.

The game of poker proceeds. You have a pair of jacks—not bad to begin with. The betting starts off high. You draw three more cards. They are worthless, but you smile just a little in hopes of fooling the others. You look at the faces around the table and make your bet. As the betting continues, you look at your jacks again and begin to worry that someone may have a better hand. You realize you might win a lot by betting very high. If your bluff works, the others will drop out. Unless you are willing to bluff, you might as well drop out yourself.

If you bluff, turn to page 56.

If you drop out, turn to page 57.

You go over to another table. One of the players looks up and says, "New in town? Have a seat and we'll deal you in. We're just playing for small stakes."

You join them and play a few hands. After a while, you begin to suspect that Ben Tuttle, a tall, gray-bearded man, has been cheating.

If you decide to confront Ben Tuttle with your suspicions, turn to page 58.

If you decide not to challenge him but just to keep playing, turn to page 59.

The next day, Jake gives up and rides on back to town. But your patience is rewarded, for Lefty soon finds a vein of gold, and the two of you are able to extract several nuggets of high-quality ore. Lefty's good fortune only seems to make him greedy, however, and he tells you that he is going to keep it all for himself.

You walk up to him slowly. "Lefty," you say, "we're partners in this deal. You can't take all that gold for yourself."

Lefty looks at you. "Maybe we were partners to begin with," he says, "but I've just decided we ain't no more. I'm keeping this gold. If you don't like it, you'd better clear out of here."

If you decide to fight Lefty right then and there, turn to page 60.

If you decide to pursue him at a distance and wait for the right moment to have it out with him, turn to page 62.

If you decide to ride back to Deadwood City for assistance, turn to page 63.

You are tempted to head across the desert for Silver Springs, which you have heard is a pretty lively town, but since you are not far from the Morning Star Ranch, you ride over there to check it out. They offer you work as a ranch hand and you think the job would be enjoyable, yet you wonder if you might find something more exciting in Silver Springs.

If you decide to stay at the Morning Star Ranch, turn to page 92.

If you decide to ride across the desert toward Silver Springs, turn to page 94.

You enter the Navaho village. The Indians greet you warmly. They have wanted to learn English for a long time.

The Indians treat you well, and while you teach them English you begin to learn about their customs and ceremonies. They make delicious corn cakes and cook wild turkey. Before long you have become a good shot with a bow and arrow.

After several months most of the Indians have learned to speak some English. You tell them you want to return to your own people. They thank you and give you some bracelets and rings of turquoise and silver.

As you leave the chief says, "We are your friends forever!"

The End

You keep riding along the trail. At sundown, you come to the Lazy Circle Ranch. The owner says he'd like to hire you, but there is something about the place you do not like. The cattle seem underfed and listless. Still, you need rest and food and a place to work.

If you decide to take the job,
turn to page 64.

If you decide to ride on toward
the next town, turn to page 65.

After you've seen some of the town you go back to the hotel for the night. Fortunately things have quieted down, and you can get a good night's sleep.

The next morning you saddle up early and ride out to the Eagle Ranch. As you approach, you observe a couple of wooden frame buildings, a barn, and a large corral. Peering over the fence is one of the finest-looking longhorn bulls you have ever seen.

Before the meeting of the Stock Owners' Association even starts you line up a job. The owner of the Eagle spread, a friendly woman named Mae, says you can work for her. She suggests that you attend the meeting so you'll know what's going on.

At the meeting the cattlemen all say that too many sheep ranchers have been moving into the area and that their sheep may kill off the grass by cropping it too close to the ground. It looks like a range war is brewing, and that means bad trouble.

If you decide to take the job at the Eagle Ranch anyway, turn to page 67.

If you decide to ride on to Silver Springs and look for a job there instead, turn to page 95.

Running a newspaper sounds great, and you gladly accept Mrs. Megan's offer. Your paper, the *Deadwood Dispatch,* will appear every Friday so that when people come into town for the weekend they can read the latest news. You'll turn over to her any money you take in on the first four issues, and after that you'll own the printing press free and clear.

While you are getting your first edition ready, many of the local cattle ranchers go out of their way to tell you that sheep are ruining the grass on the open range by cropping it too close to the ground.

An editorial on the subject will certainly attract attention to your newspaper. The cattlemen's position sounds convincing, and you think maybe you'll say in the *Dispatch* that the sheep ranchers should go back where they came from.

If you do decide to write an editorial against the sheep ranchers, turn to page 26.

If you decide to wait until you have heard the sheep ranchers' side, turn to page 27.

You pack up and head west toward Silver Springs. As you are riding along, a band of Indians comes galloping down from the hills and surrounds you. There is no chance to escape. You surrender, and they take you back to their camp.

The camp is large, probably several hundred people. Many of the women are preparing meat and stretching buffalo skins after a successful hunt. Your captors tell you to sit and wait near the edge of the encampment.

After what seems like hours, the chief himself walks up to you. He stands silently for a long time, looking you in the eye. Finally he says, "You fear us. We fear the white men. What can you do for us?"

You sit there thinking. The chief walks off.

At last you have an idea: you could offer to help the Indians make an agreement with the white men that would protect their hunting grounds. But you also notice that no one is guarding you, and you could probably jump on the horse tied up nearby and ride off on it.

If you decide to offer to help effect an agreement with the white men, turn to page 75.

If you rush to the horse in an effort to escape, turn to page 76.

You miss Kurt Malloy completely, but he shoots you in the right leg, and you sink to the ground.

"I'm letting you off easy this time," Malloy says as he returns his gun to his holster. Then he and

his buddies gallop off, leaving you lying in the dust.

Some people come running out of the saloon, and they help you up and take you to a doctor. Fortunately, your wound is not serious, and after a few days' rest you feel strong enough to leave town.

If you decide to go after Malloy and try to get even, turn to page 73.

If you decide to forget about Malloy and leave Deadwood City, turn to page 74.

You walk up to Kurt Malloy and look him in the eye.

"You're new to these parts, aren't you?" he says. "Well, you don't seem like a bad sort to me. I like you. In fact, I'm going to give you a real big chance. I'm going to let you join us. You'll get rich so fast you won't know what happened to you."

If you decide to join the gang, turn to page 25.

If you decide you'll pretend to join the gang and try to bring them to justice, turn to page 71.

If you decide not to join them, turn to page 72.

You don't look back as you walk down the street, and Malloy calls out, "You turn your back on me and you might find a bullet in it!"

You keep walking, figuring that even Kurt Malloy won't shoot someone in the back. Fortunately, you are right. He and his buddies ride off in the opposite direction

Once you are safely out of range, you decide to look around town.

Turn to page 15.

When Malloy returns from the saloon, you and your new companions go to the sheriff's office. Malloy kicks open the door and walks in. You and the others follow.

"Thanks for inviting me in, sheriff," Malloy says. "I'm glad to see you and I are going to be such good friends."

The sheriff just stands there saying nothing. He tries to look tough, but you can see he is very frightened.

Just then one of Malloy's men, who has been keeping watch, announces that an armed posse is coming down the street. Malloy and his buddies rush out the door, jump on their horses, and ride off at a gallop. You are left behind. Luckily the sheriff doesn't realize that you were part of the gang.

If you decide to try to rejoin Malloy and his friends, turn to page 78.

If you decide to have nothing more to do with Kurt Malloy, turn to page 79.

You continue to take the sheep ranchers' side in your editorials, but a few days later you find that your office has been broken into, your printing press damaged, and type scattered all over the place. You call the sheriff in. He says Kurt Malloy's gang must be responsible, but you feel sure some cattlemen are behind it.

As soon as you can get your press repaired, you print a special edition. Your headline reads, NO FREE PRESS MEANS NO FREEDOM. You call on the

people of Deadwood City to get a new sheriff and enough good deputies to enforce the law. After that, many people come to your office and pledge their help. A protective committee is formed to end lawlessness in Deadwood City.

You realize that there may still be trouble ahead, but you enjoy your work and you are determined to make the *Deadwood Dispatch* the best newspaper in the West.

The End

You avoid writing about the problems between cattle ranchers and sheep ranchers in the *Deadwood Dispatch,* but every new topic you discuss seems to bring you new enemies.

After a few months you decide that running a newspaper in Deadwood City is a thankless job. You know you can sell your printing press for enough money to buy a stagecoach ticket to San Francisco, where you can start a new life and a new career, and that's what you do.

The End

For a time you don't run any editorials in the *Deadwood Dispatch*, but you do print letters from cattle ranchers who believe sheep should be kept off the open range and from sheep ranchers who feel they have as much right to it as the cattlemen.

Eventually you decide that sheep ranchers are in the West to stay, and that cattlemen must respect their right to share the public grazing lands. You write editorials expressing your new opinion, and soon you receive many complaining letters. But most people respect you for stating your own views and reporting fairly the views of others, and your policy enables you to sell more and more copies of the *Deadwood Dispatch*.

The End

You run another editorial supporting the cattlemen. Although you still have doubts, you feel that people may lose respect for you if you argue on one side one day and on another side the next. Besides, some of your best friends are cattle ranchers.

But in the months ahead, things do not go well with your newspaper. You can't sell enough copies to make a living. No one seems interested in what you write. Finally you have to sell the *Deadwood Dispatch* to some men who own a big cattle ranch in the area. You want to stay in newspaper work, however, and you go back East to Chicago, where you get a job as a typesetter for the *Chicago Tribune* and settle down to life in the big city.

The End

You ride with the gold shipment to San Francisco. On the first day of the trip, you have to go through a pass between two great rock walls. You round a bend only to find that the trail has been mostly washed out by a flash flood. It is getting late in the day. Scotty MacLeod, the driver of the coach, asks if you think he should try to get through even though you may get stuck.

While inspecting the trail, you find evidence of a recent campfire. It could mean bandits are in the area—and this would be an ideal place for a holdup.

If you tell Scotty he should try to get through as fast as possible, *turn to page 80.*

If you decide to wait and try to find out whether there are bandits nearby, *turn to page 100.*

You ride with the mail coach along the trail that winds around the Beaver Tail Mountains. The slopes above you are covered with wild flowers. In the distance you see a herd of buffalo.

It is a peaceful scene, but the stagecoach driver is worried. He shakes his head. "This is Indian country," he says, "and some of them don't like us riding through their land."

Almost as soon as he has spoken, you notice three Indians on spotted horses riding toward you. You jump to the ground and draw your gun, but one Indian holds up his right hand in a sign of peace. Should you go toward them? They may be trying to trick you.

If you walk toward the Indians and return the peace sign, turn to page 82.

If you prepare to shoot it out, turn to page 83.

You just walk away from Larson, and you try to keep out of his way. But the very next day at dawn, you are awakened by something cold moving across your leg. Startled, you pull back the blanket and look down upon a diamondback rattlesnake. You leap out of bed a split second before it strikes. Then you see Larson sneaking out of the bunkhouse.

You realize now that you will have to take action. Larson is determined to get rid of you one way or another.

If you decide to have it out with Larson,
turn to page 84.

If you decide to get proof that he is trying to do you in so you can have him dealt with by the law,
turn to page 85.

You discuss Larson's behavior with Mr. Griswold.

"Thanks for telling me, kid," he says, "but I'm not about to pick a fight with Larson. Anyway, I need him on the ranch."

You are disgusted with Griswold's weakness.

If you decide to quit and leave the Red Creek Ranch, turn to page 41.

If you decide to try to persuade Griswold to do something, turn to page 86.

Your bluff works. The others drop out, and you rake in the chips.

One young cowhand looks at you and says, "All I can say, pal, is you're some poker player!"

Some of the people have lost so much money that they have to quit, but a couple of them are left. One says to you, "Say, how about one more round, double or nothing?"

It is a tempting thought. You are having a run of good luck tonight, and this could be your chance to make it really big.

If you decide to quit and keep the money you have already won, turn to page 88.

If you decide to take one more chance and see if you can really clean up, turn to page 90.

You quit the game. At least you avoided being wiped out. As you walk out of the saloon, you stop to talk to a couple of people standing by the bar.

One of them says, "Looks like you had some bad luck. Well, tomorrow's another day."

"Yeah," you say, "but tomorrow I need to get myself a job."

"I hear there's a job notice posted at the general store," he answers. "I don't know what it is, maybe nothing much, but you might want to check it out."

You decide that would be a good thing to do.

Turn to page 15.

"I saw you dealing off the bottom of the deck," you say. "Now I want all the money you've won divided up fairly, and then I want you to get out of here."

Ben Tuttle just sits there looking at you, his mean little eyes squinting in the glare of the kerosene lantern swinging over your table.

"I don't like being called a cheater, especially by a greenhorn like you," he says.

"I don't like being cheated," you say.

"I see you're packing a gun. Step outside and draw."

You stand up and walk toward the entrance, but as you pass through the swinging doors, you hear Tuttle call after you, "I'll be along in a while. I want to give you time to practice your shooting."

You realize that Tuttle has no intention of fighting you. You decide not to hang around any longer. Deadwood City is not the place for you, and you'd rather try your luck elsewhere.

Turn to page 41.

You decide not to challenge Ben Tuttle, since you're not absolutely sure he is cheating. You stay in the game, and the play goes on. You lose again and again. You wish you had confronted Tuttle or quit earlier, but now it's too late. You're nearly wiped out. You leave the game and walk over to the bar.

You know you'll have to get a job soon. The easiest course might be to ask for work right there in the saloon. The bartender suggests that you wait until the owner comes in. "Or you might talk to Mrs. Megan, down the street," he says. "If anyone has work for you, she'll know about it."

If you decide to go talk to Mrs. Megan, turn to page 14.

If you decide to wait for the saloon owner, turn to page 91.

You move a few paces away. Lefty stands up. You notice his left hand slowly dropping toward his holster. "All right, pal," he says. "You made a big mistake tangling with me."

"You can't do this, Lefty," you say. But Lefty draws and shoots. At the same time you draw your gun and fire—shooting his gun right out of his hand.

"I should have you tried for attempted murder," you say. "Now clear out of here!"

"Can't I even have my share of the gold?" Lefty whines.

You tell him he is lucky to get away with his life and, after taking away his guns, you send him off on his horse. You head back to Deadwood City. This time you will be riding into town with a smile on your face and a pouch of gold in your saddlebag.

The End

You ride a little way off, keeping an eye on Lefty. He heads down the trail to the west. You figure that he's bound for Silver Springs. You gallop across a shortcut over the mesa until you reach a pass. There you lie in wait for him.

Just about dusk, you hear the sound of hoofbeats. You look over the top of the ridge. It's Lefty, all right! He passes only a few feet in front of you, and you raise your rifle, calling out, "Okay, Lefty, this is it! We're going to share that gold or you're going to make a meal for the vultures."

Lefty stops, smiles, and says, "Okay, you win," but suddenly he reaches for his gun. You try to shoot it out of his hand. Your bullet only grazes his arm, but he drops his gun and begs for mercy. You force him to hand over his saddlebags, which are weighted down with all the gold. Then you tell him to ride away and keep out of your sight.

After Lefty has disappeared over the horizon, you load the gold onto your horse and head on to the next town, whistling your favorite tune.

The End

You ride back to town and report to the sheriff that Lefty is stealing your gold, but the sheriff refuses to help. He has Kurt Malloy to worry about. Besides, he knows it would only be your word against Lefty's.

Now there is no way you can catch up with Lefty. You are stuck in Deadwood City without any money. Somehow you will have to get a job and start all over again.

The End

You go to work at the Lazy Circle Ranch. Things go smoothly there, but the work is tedious—mostly chores around the corral. Some weeks later, you hear there is a lot of trouble in town. Kurt Malloy and his gang have taken over. You are thankful just to have a safe place to live.

But soon winter comes. The wind howls and the snow piles up around your bunkhouse. Often you have only half a can of beans for dinner. You spend the evenings huddled by the wood stove, wondering whether somehow you couldn't find a better life.

The End

You ride down the trail in the direction of Silver Springs. After traveling for a couple of days, you know you must be more than halfway there, but you have run out of water.

You are very thirsty, and you know there is a water hole beyond the next mesa. The trip there would take you several hours out of your way, but at least you know you could make it there, find water, and fill your canteen. However, you are desperately hungry. You have no provisions, and there is no place to get food this side of Silver Springs.

If you decide to head for the water hole,
turn to page 106.

If you decide to try to make it to
Silver Springs without getting water,
turn to page 107.

You ride out to the Sunrise Ranch at noon the next day. The work Jim Putney describes to you sounds rough, and he says, "I have to warn you—the cattle ranchers are trying to keep our sheep off public land, and they've even been taking potshots at us." But you are convinced there is a great future in sheep ranching, and you want to give it a try.

Soon after you start work, however, you find that some of your sheep are missing, and you discover that they have fallen off a cliff.

"This isn't the first time this has happened," Jim tells you. "The cattlemen are out to ruin us. What do you think should be done?"

Two possibilities occur to you.

If you decide to take a trip to petition the territorial legislature for better laws and enforcement, turn to page 96.

If you decide to get other sheep ranchers together and enforce the law yourself, turn to page 110.

A few days later you and some of the cattle ranchers ride out toward the new sheep ranch to discuss the situation with the owners. On the way you come upon a stretch of new barbed wire fence.

"These varmints have been fencing off grazing land. They're trying to ruin us," Mae says. She has hardly finished speaking when about ten men come riding up. They carry shotguns as well as side arms. You realize they are sheep ranchers.

"No use reaching for your gun," Mae warns you. "We're outnumbered."

The leader of the sheep ranchers calls over sarcastically, "It's been nice having you visit, but now we'd be obliged if you'd get off our property."

You and your companions have no choice but to retreat to the Eagle Ranch.

"We'll just have to make the best of it till we can get more help," Mae says.

You never do get enough help to drive out the sheep ranchers, though. Finally you have to settle for less grazing land. But a few years later you make up for it by raising some prize-winning bulls that bring you fame and fortune.

The End

You take the job at the T-Bar Ranch, but as time goes by, you find the work boring. Worst of all, the food is terrible. After a few weeks, you pack up and head for California to search for gold.

The End

You join the posse. All of you have horses and guns. Everyone knows that Kurt Malloy has a campsite a few miles outside of town, and you figure the gang will probably be heading back to their camp.

You and the others in the posse ride out to try to cut the badmen off at the pass. One man stands up on a rock outcropping to watch. After a while, he whistles. That means Malloy and his gang are approaching. When they come riding through the pass, you are ready. You and the rest of the posse ride down so fast that you catch them off guard.

They throw down their guns, and all that's left for you to do is march them back to town and collect a big reward. As you come riding down the main street, everyone comes out waving and cheering. Now law-abiding citizens can safely walk the streets of Deadwood City.

Soon afterward, you get a job as a carpenter. Almost everyone likes you and admires your workmanship. You finally make enough money to buy your own ranch, where you raise the biggest longhorn bull anyone has ever seen, and your reputation spreads far and wide.

The End

You tell Malloy you'll join him, figuring that you'll learn enough about the gang's plans to help put them behind bars. After having a drink at the saloon, Malloy gets you and his buddies together for a conference. He says he heard at the saloon that the stagecoach leaving for San Francisco will be loaded with gold, and he plans to hold it up.

"We'll ride out at five o'clock tomorrow and meet the stagecoach at the pass at six," he says. The first chance you get, you slip away and warn the sheriff.

The next day you ride out to the pass with Malloy and his gang. When you spot the sheriff coming, you raise your shotgun and say, "You're under arrest, Kurt!" Some of the members of the sheriff's posse ride up from the other direction. Malloy and his gang are surrounded; they have to surrender. You and the sheriff take them in. You soon find you have made quite a name for yourself in Deadwood City.

The End

Rather than join up with Malloy, you run away as fast as you can.

One of the men in Malloy's gang pulls out his gun and is about to shoot you, but Malloy stops him. "Don't bother," he says. "That kid isn't worth a bullet."

You are happy that for the time being Kurt Malloy is not interested in killing you. You decide to get out of town before he changes his mind.

Turn to page 36.

You vow to get Malloy as soon as you have a chance. A week later, you are sitting in the saloon when the bartender tells you the news: Malloy and his gang are coming back into Deadwood City. They have already held up most of the shopkeepers in town, and now they have their eyes on the bank.

You put down some money and walk out through the swinging doors into the bright sunlight. There, a few hundred feet down the street, are Malloy and his gang—heading toward the bank. You know a U.S. marshal has just checked into the hotel.

If you decide to go get the U.S. marshal, turn to page 97.

If you decide to go right out and confront Malloy, turn to page 99.

You hit the trail for the next town. The weather is good, and when you arrive you have no trouble getting a job at nearby Tumbleweed Ranch. It looks promising. The people are nice, and the food is good. After you have been there a week, the owner is so pleased with your work that he gives you a guitar. You enjoy sitting around the fire playing your guitar and singing with the other ranch hands. It often occurs to you that the smartest thing you ever did was to get out of Deadwood City.

The End

You tell the chief that you believe you could help the Indians reach an agreement with the white men. You know that the Bureau of Indian Affairs has opened an office in Denver and that its job is to protect the rights of Indians as well as to resolve land disputes between the Indians and white men. After finding out what the Indians want and what they are willing to give, you set out for Denver to see what you can accomplish.

On the way you begin to wonder if you should bother. You ask yourself, "What's in it for me?"

If you decide to keep your word and try to help the Indians, turn to page 108.

If you are just happy to get away from the Indians, turn to page 109.

You run for the horse. It is a big, powerful animal, and you know it can travel. But it is tied to a tree. You do not have a knife, and it takes you a moment to untie the knot. Someone is yelling at you, but you leap on the horse and begin to ride off. You do not get far. . . .

The End

You ride to the abandoned farmhouse where you know Malloy and his gang are hiding out.

"Glad to see you back," Malloy says, "We've shown them we're tough. We've shown them that we can easily take over the sheriff's office. We just need a little time. The people of this town are too yellow to fight us. Right, pal?" Malloy looks you square in the eye.

"Right," you say.

Just then there is the sound of hoofbeats approaching. It is the citizens' posse—they have tracked you down.

"Come out, Malloy," calls someone from the posse. "We have you surrounded. You and your buddies come out, hands up, right now!"

You have no choice but to surrender. You are tried and convicted. It is two and a half years before you are released from jail.

The End

You go to the saloon and sit down to think things over. You're not so sure it's good to be on Malloy's side in this town. On the other hand, things don't look too good for the sheriff's side either.

As you are sitting there feeling depressed, a cowhand from the Fulton Ranch strikes up a conversation. You tell him you would just as soon get out of Deadwood City, and he suggests that you ride out to his ranch the next day, because they need extra cowhands for a cattle drive to the East. That sounds like just the change of scene you need, and a couple of days later you are on your way to Missouri, helping drive one of the biggest herds of cattle that ever crossed the range.

The End

The stagecoach makes good progress for a while, but the trail is rocky and rough. Soon you come to a place with very deep ruts. Driving across it could wreck the coach. Still, what lies behind you is almost as bad. You cross your fingers as Scotty urges the horses on.

As soon as you get going again, the coach hits a tremendous rut, breaking the rear axle. While you

are trying to fix it, a man comes riding up the trail. He has a shotgun aimed right at you, and you realize he must be the bandits' lookout. You exchange fire and scare him off, but you know he'll be back—with reinforcements.

Turn to page 105.

You lay down your gun and walk toward them holding out your hands, palms up, to show that you are not armed. The Indians come up to you. You have trouble talking with them at first, but gradually you begin to understand one another. They want salt and ammunition. You give them a supply of each, and they give you some Indian blankets in return and wish you good fortune.

You continue on to Santa Fe, pleased with the way you have handled yourself. When you arrive, you decide to settle there and never return to Deadwood City.

The End

You decide it is too risky to trust the Indians, and you raise your gun and start shooting. Soon you realize you are hopelessly outnumbered. In a moment, you feel the searing pain of an arrow and then another. It is all over for you.

The End

Late that afternoon you see Larson. He is inspecting the fence. You call to him from a distance of about thirty yards, "I'm not going to let you get away with this, Larson!"

Larson reaches for his Colt revolver and fires before you can react. The first shot grazes your leg, but his gun jams and he cannot fire again.

You point your gun at him. "Drop it!" you say. Larson reluctantly tosses his gun on the ground. You march him into the main house. Mr. Griswold tells Larson his next stop will be the county jail.

After Larson has been tried, convicted, and sent to jail, everyone on the Red Creek Ranch feels a lot better. You are especially happy, because Mr. Griswold makes you his manager.

The End

You decide to let Mr. Griswold see for himself that Larson is trying to do you in.

Pete Sommers, one of the ranch hands, owns a huge, poisonous spider—a tarantula—that he keeps in a glass-topped box. One day, Pete tells you that his tarantula has just disappeared. You figure Larson probably plans to put the spider in your bed before you turn in for the night.

That evening you persuade Mr. Griswold to hide with you near your sleeping quarters. Sure enough, while the two of you are watching, Larson sneaks in and puts the tarantula in your bunk. As Larson leaves, you and Griswold jump him from behind. The next day, you and Griswold ride into town with Larson and hand him over to the sheriff.

When you return, Griswold makes you his manager. A few years later, he retires and moves back East. By then, you have saved up enough money to become the new owner of the Red Creek Ranch.

The End

You stay at the ranch and have another talk with Mr. Griswold. You bring a friendly cowhand along, and the two of you point out that unless someone stops Larson, there will be serious trouble. This time Griswold listens to what you say.

The next day, he calls Larson in and says, "Larson, you're fired! Pack up and hit the trail!" Larson snarls and curses, but Griswold is firm. Finally Larson stalks out, gets his gear together, and rides off at a gallop.

Years later you learn that he has been convicted of armed robbery and now resides in the Colorado State Penitentiary.

The End

You take off with your winnings, but as you're walking toward the door, you hear some people talking about you.

One of the cowhands standing at the bar says, "Hey, look at that kid. That kid's going to be really rich—at least for a couple of hours."

Another one says as you walk by, "Good luck today, bad luck tomorrow."

You decide the smartest thing to do is to leave Deadwood City. You don't think much of the town even without Kurt Malloy.

You hit the trail and ride on. You know you can reach Silver Springs in three days and find a place to stay. You have enough provisions to last for the trip. You will have to sleep out in the mountains a couple of nights. It will be plenty cold, but you can take it. You have more money than you ever had before. Life looks pretty good.

The End

WANTED

The cards are dealt out. You have two fives, a nine, and two queens. You wonder if it is even worth keeping the pair of fives. Might be better to throw them down and try for three queens. You look around and see the cold, hard eyes staring at you. One guy takes only one card, another takes none. You throw down the two fives and keep the queens. But in the new draw, you get nothing. The dealer has a pair of sixes and a pair of jacks. Tough luck for you.

You walk out of the saloon, feeling worse than you ever have before. You do not even have enough money to stay at the hotel overnight.

You decide to try to catch some sleep at Horace Wheeler's livery stable. Tomorrow maybe you'll ride on to Silver Springs and see if life is any better for you there than in Deadwood City.

The End

You talk with the owner and get a job sweeping out the saloon. The pay is low; your food is scraps from the kitchen. They give you a place to sleep that looks like a chicken coop. It will take you months to scrape together enough cash to buy provisions and hit the trail. For the moment, you have no choice but to stay on the job; you have to eat. And you figure that one job is as good as another. But you decide that Deadwood City is no place for you. As soon as you can save up a little money, you will pack up and head for California.

The End

You stay on as a cowhand at the Morning Star Ranch. It is a great place to live. You especially like riding the range, breathing the fresh air, and looking up at the stars and listening to the coyotes howl at the moon. You feel as if you might just stay forever.

The End

The next morning at sunrise you are on your horse and on your way again, bound for Silver Springs. Unfortunately, the second day out, you get lost. You know you are headed in the right direction but you cannot locate the trail.

To make matters worse, you run out of water and food. The weather has been hot. Clouds of dust swirl in the wind.

You wonder what to do. If you keep going straight ahead without getting water, you may not make it. You know there is likely to be water to the north or to the south.

If you decide to go north,
turn to page 102.

If you decide to go south,
turn to page 104.

When you arrive at Silver Springs after a three-day ride, everyone in town is celebrating. They have just received word that the railroad being built from St. Louis to points west will pass through Silver Springs.

You drop into the saloon for a bite to eat and strike up a conversation with one of the surveyors from the railroad. He says that if you're willing to ride to Topeka, you will have no trouble getting a job with the Atchison, Topeka & Santa Fe Railroad.

You feel certain that the coming of the railroads will really open up the West. If you could get the right job, you could travel all over the country. So the next day you hit the trail for Kansas and a new life.

The End

You ride to Santa Fe, where the territorial legislature is meeting, only to find that the politicians have no interest in your story. Finally, one of them tells you that most of the legislators are friends of cattle owners, and some of them are even on the payroll of the Stock Owners' Association.

When you get back to the Sunrise Ranch and report this news, Jim Putney shakes his head in disgust. "Well," he says, "things aren't going to be easy. We'll just have to keep a close watch on our sheep, and if we can't keep as much stock, we'll have to get higher prices for what we sell."

For the next few years work is hard and the pay is low at the Sunrise Ranch. But finally good things begin to happen. Most important, the railroad finally reaches Deadwood City. After that you can send stock East by train. The ranch prospers, and you become general manager.

The End

You run at top speed to the hotel and quickly find the marshal. You tell him that Kurt Malloy is headed toward the bank.

The Tyler brothers, who run the general store right across the street, had previously volunteered as deputies, and at a call from the marshal they come running out. The four of you rush to the bank.

Malloy and his buddies are already inside, holding up the cashier. In a moment they come out, carrying over ten thousand dollars in greenbacks.

As the outlaws run out of the bank, you and the marshal and the Tyler brothers run up crying out, "Reach for the sky!" One of Malloy's men foolishly fires, but he is immediately felled by the

Go on to the next page.

marshal. Malloy, who is a coward at heart, surrenders and begs for mercy. The marshal comes up and shakes your hand.

"Good work," he says. "You'll be getting a good share of the reward for the capture of Kurt Malloy!"

The End

You step out into Malloy's path and say, "Now it's my turn! Draw!"

He draws, of course, as you do. You are faster on the draw, but your shot goes over his head as he ducks. You hear his bullet whistle past your ear. Then you feel a gun in your back. It is one of Malloy's henchmen.

"You're going to ride straight out of town," he says, "and if we ever see you around here again, we'll finish you off."

You have no choice but to do as you are told. You saddle up and head out onto the trail, wondering whether law and justice will ever come to Deadwood City.

The End

You and Scotty MacLeod climb up on some rocks; from there you have a good view of the surrounding countryside. In the distance, you see a couple of men coming up the trail. You lie there quietly with your guns ready. The men cautiously approach the stagecoach and look around nervously, but do not see you hidden among the rocks.

You and Scotty watch as they reach into the coach and start to lift out the strongbox containing the gold. Then you leap down and shout, "Up with your hands!" You take their guns and make them ride ahead of you back to town.

Almost all the people in Deadwood City come out to greet you with cheers, and the stagecoach

company gives you a big bonus for doing a great job riding shotgun.

The End

For a while, you feel as if you are going nowhere. Then up ahead you see some flat-topped rocks that look as if they might form a catch basin. Your guess was right, and you soon find all the water you can use. From your vantage point, you can see the Snake River in the distance, and you know that from there you can find the trail to Silver Springs.

You saddle up and continue your journey. The going is rough, but at least you're not lost anymore. Though you're still hungry, you know you can survive as long as you have water.

Turn to page 19.

You go south looking for water. You have no luck, and you and your horse are becoming exhausted. Finally you have to stop and rest in the shade of some rocks until the sun gets lower. You lie back and close your eyes, not realizing that a rattlesnake is slithering toward you.

Half asleep, you barely hear its rattling, but as your dulled senses begin to work, you freeze. For what seems like a very long time you lie absolutely still, afraid even to breathe.

When the snake finally glides away, you get back on your horse and resume your weary journey.

Turn to page 106.

You and Scotty decide the only thing to do is hide the gold and head back to town for help. You conceal the strongbox in a cave behind some tangled brush, unhitch the horses, and ride to Deadwood City. There you enlist the sheriff and some others to return with you.

When you arrive, you find that bandits have ransacked the stagecoach. Fortunately, they did not find the gold you hid so carefully. You are given a raise and a bonus for your good work, and soon you are riding shotgun again, enjoying the risks and rewards of working in the frontier.

The End

Fortunately, it is not as far to the water hole as you feared. You reach it in a couple of hours. You and your horse drink your fill, and you splash your head and face with cool, clear water. Soon you are on the trail again.

At sundown the next day, you reach Silver Springs, where you meet an old friend of your family. He invites you to stay on his comfortable ranch while you are looking for a job. It looks like a halfway decent town—a lot better place to live than Deadwood City.

The End

You head across the desert trying to find the way to Silver Springs. Unfortunately, the town is much farther away than you thought. There has been no rain for a long time, and whatever water holes there might have been along the way have dried up. After a couple of days, you wish you had never started out, but by this time it is too late to turn back. You continue on, weary and thirsty, but you never make it to Silver Springs.

The End

When you arrive in Denver, you find the Bureau of Indian Affairs man in his office. He is happy to hear that the Indians want to negotiate, because he was afraid they were getting ready to go on the warpath.

He accompanies you to the Indians' camp and promises the Indians that they can keep their lands if they will not attack the white men. The Indians are grateful to you for your help. They give you gifts of turquoise beads, blankets, and gold nuggets.

You thank them heartily and bid them good-bye, but just before you ride off, the chief quietly says to you, "My heart is still heavy, for we can no more trust the white man to keep his promise than the moon to keep its shape."

The End

You feel that you do not owe the Indians anything. There is no point in going all the way to Denver. You might return to Deadwood City, which isn't far away. Or you might head across the desert to continue your journey to Silver Springs.

If you decide to head back toward Deadwood City, turn to page 38.

If you decide to stay on the trail to Silver Springs, turn to page 112.

The next day you ride around to the other sheep ranchers in the area and ask them to come to a meeting at the Sunrise Ranch.

You all agree to put up more barbed wire around your ranches and to send people to the various cattlemen to warn them to keep away.

A few days later, though, you get a report that the cattle ranchers are fencing off a water hole on public land. A group of you ride out and cut down the fence so your sheep can get water. Just as you are finishing the job, some cattlemen come riding up. You warn them to leave the water hole open or else. They yell and curse at you, but finally turn their horses and ride off. As they get up speed, one of them turns and takes a parting shot at you.

"We don't need to chase them," Jim Putney says. "If we just defend our rights, we'll survive."

Life is rough for a while, but you work hard and eventually become manager of the Sunrise Ranch. A few years later you settle down, get married, and begin to raise a family. All in all, you couldn't wish for a better life.

The End

111

You ride on across the hot, dusty sand, trying to make it to Silver Springs, but it is no use. There are few water holes, and you have no idea how to find them; the streams are all dried up. Your horse becomes too weak to go on, and you continue on foot. You become delirious with thirst and walk straight into the path of a rattlesnake. You are too far gone even to feel its bite. In a few hours, you are just another piece of the history of the West.

The End

ABOUT THE AUTHOR

A graduate of Princeton University and Columbia Law School, EDWARD PACKARD lives in New York City, where he is a practicing lawyer. Mr. Packard conceived of the idea for the Choose Your Own Adventure® series in the course of telling bedtime stories to his children, Caroline, Andrea, and Wells.

ABOUT THE ILLUSTRATOR

PAUL GRANGER is a prize-winning illustrator and painter.